W9-CZM-438

BURGESS TRADE QUADDIES MARK

Smiling Pool Series

Jerry Muskrat At Home

By

THORNTON W. BURGESS

With Illustrations by

HARRISON CADY

G D

Grosset & Dunlap

PUBLISHERS NEW YORK

ISBN: 0-448-02803-4 (TRADE EDITION)
ISBN: 0-448-13739-9 (LIBRARY EDITION)

BY ARRANGEMENT WITH LITTLE, BROWN, AND COMPANY
PRINTED IN THE UNITED STATES OF AMERICA

CONTENTS

CONTENTS

ILLUSTRATIONS

"MAYBE WE WON'T HAVE A BAD WINTER," INTERRUPTED PETER. *Frontispiece.* *See page 21.*

Jerry Muskrat at Home

CHAPTER I

PETER RABBIT GROWS IMPATIENT

Who does the work at hand to-day,
To-morrow may have time to play.
Jerry Muskrat.

JERRY MUSKRAT was building a new house. Every evening that the way seemed clear and safe, Peter Rabbit scampered across from the dear Old Briar-patch to the Smiling Pool to see how Jerry was getting on. Peter's curiosity was impatient. Curiosity is apt to be impatient. He wanted to see the walls of that new house rise out of the water, but night after night he was disappointed.

There was n't a thing above water to show that Jerry Muskrat was building a house there. There was just the muddy water and occasionally the head of Jerry, as he came up for a breath of fresh air, to show that something was going on down in the Smiling Pool.

After a few nights of this sort of thing, Peter began to be doubtful. He began to doubt if Jerry Muskrat was really building a house at all. He said as much to Grandfather Frog. "It seems to me," said he, "that there ought to be some signs of that house if there is ever going to be one. I'm beginning to think that it is all a bluff on Jerry Muskrat's part. I don't believe he is building a house at all. He has been working long enough to have built two houses, it seems to me, yet there is n't a thing to show for it.

Grandfather Frog rolled his great goggly eyes up at Peter, sitting on the bank, and stretched his big mouth in the broadest of grins. "Perhaps," said he softly, "you think you could build that house better and faster than Jerry can."

Peter looked a wee bit foolish, just a wee bit foolish. He had never built a house in his life and he knew that Grandfather Frog knew it. "Just the same, I think he is terribly slow about it," he protested. "If it takes him as long as all this just to get the foundations laid, it will take him the rest of the year to finish the job, and cold weather will come before then."

Grandfather Frog chuckled. "A lot you know about it, Peter," said he. "A lot you know about it. I suppose you think that the biggest part of the work on that house is what will have to be done above water. Let me tell you something, Peter: The part of that house which you will see when it is finished is the easiest part of the work Jerry has to do. You ought to learn to dive, Peter, and then you would see and learn a lot you don't know now and never will know." Peter looked wistfully and longingly down into the Smiling Pool. "I wish I could," said he. "I certainly wish I could." Then, as he noted how muddy the water was, he suddenly changed his mind. "I guess I'm just as well satisfied not to," said he. "I'll take your word for it that there are interesting things down there under water. I know this, that if I could dive, I never would open my eyes in any such muddy water as that.

Grandfather Frog laughed. You know he does n't mind muddy water at all. In fact, when he goes to the bottom of the Smiling Pool, he goes right down into the mud itself. It seemed funny to him that any one should mind muddy water. He rather liked it himself, because in it he could disappear so easily. Peter looked over to where the mud was being stirred up by Jerry Muskrat at work down below. "Just the same," said Peter, "I do think Jerry is a long time building this house."

CHAPTER II

WHAT JERRY MUSKRAT WAS DOING

Do what you do with all your might,
But first make sure you start it right.
Jerry Muskrat.

DID you ever watch a house built? Of course you have. You know how first of all a cellar is dug. You know how sewer and water pipes are laid. You know that a lot of work is done in the ground which does n't go into the house itself, but which is a part of the building of the house just the same.

It was this same way with Jerry Muskrat and his new house. He had a lot to do before he could build the house itself, which would rise above the surface of the water. Grandfather Frog had been right when he said that this part of the work would be the easiest for Jerry.

First of all, Jerry had to dig a sort of cellar. The mud from this he piled around him to make a sort of wall. It was really the beginning of the foundations of the new house. When he had this cellar finished, of course the water was quite a lot deeper there than it was around it. This was why he had dug it. He knew that the water was so shallow around it that it would very likely freeze clear to the bottom in the winter. He did n't want that to happen under his house. Or, should I say inside his house? You see, that cellar really was a part of his house. Anyway, it was the way by which he would go in and out, so it had to be made safe. It would n't do to leave a chance of being frozen in. So he took pains to make it deep enough.

Then from that cellar he started a tunnel over to the bank of the Smiling Pool. It took time to dig that tunnel. When he reached the bank, he kept right on slanting up until he had reached a place where it was dry and where he felt sure that the spring flood would not reach, unless it happened to be such an unusual flood as the one that had swept away his old house last spring. There he made a comfortable and roomy chamber. wherein he would later make a nice bed of grass.

Then Jerry went back to his cellar and started another tunnel. This one he headed straight for the deepest part of the Smiling Pool, where he knew there would be water. no matter how thick the ice above might be. When this was finished. he dug another tunnel to the bank and another to deep water. so that in case of accident to the first ones, he would still have tunnels he could use. Jerry believes in being prepared.

It takes time and a lot of hard work to dig tunnels like these. It was this that Jerry was doing while Peter Rabbit was so impatiently watching for some signs of the new house above water. The bits of earth and sod which Jerry dug out, he used to broaden the foundations around his cellar, and of course it was this work that made the water so muddy.

The truth is, these tunnels were quite as important as the house itself. In some ways they were more important. So Jerry took great pains in digging them. He knew that the time might come when his life would depend on them. He intended that if that time did come, there should be nothing wrong with those tunnels. Not until they were finished did he give much thought to the rest of the house.

CHAPTER III

SAFETY FIRST AND COMFORT NEXT

The secret of true happiness you'll find
in useful labor;
It leaves no time for discontent or envy-
ing your neighbor.
Jerry Muskrat.

If any one should ask Jerry Muskrat how to build a house, the advice he would give would be something like this: "Build it for safety first and comfort next." There is n't one of the little people of the Green Meadows and the Green Forest but will say that this is the very best of good advice. Even Peter Rabbit will say so, though, as everybody knows, he does n't live up to it. If safety means hard work, Peter will take a chance with danger every time. Even when his own comfort is concerned, Peter will avoid the work if possible. Is n't it funny how lazy and short-sighted some people can be?

But Jerry Muskrat is n't one of these. Oh, my, no! No, indeed! When he dug those tunnels from the cellar of his house down under water over to the bank and to the deepest part of the Smiling Pool, he was thinking of safety and preparing for it. And safety was his first thought as he built the walls above water. He knew that when Jack Frost should come and cover the Smiling Pool with ice, it would be an easy matter for Old Man Coyote and Reddy and Granny Fox to get to his house. If the walls were thin and poorly made, they might be torn open. Then, too, the cold might creep through and freeze him. For some reason, just why he did n't know, he had a feeling that the coming winter was going to be extra cold. So Jerry made those walls extra thick. He chose the stoutest cat-tails and rushes he could find and dug up the biggest roots he could manage. He went a little way up the Laughing Brook for sticks. All these things he towed across the Smiling Pool to the new house and worked into the walls. He dug up mud and mixed it with the rushes and cat-tails and sticks in a way that only he and Paddy the Beaver can.

Peter Rabbit, watching from the bank, turned up his nose. "It is nothing but a pile of rubbish," said he.

In truth, Peter was n't to be blamed for saying so. That is what it looked like—just a great pile of rubbish. What Peter could n't see was that in the center of it was a nice big roomy chamber, one big enough so that Jerry and two or three friends could sleep there in comfort. Not only this, but it was high enough to be dry, even though the water should rise quite a lot in the Smiling Pool. And this nice, dry chamber connected with the water cellar beneath, from which the tunnels to the bank and to deep water led.

So, while in his tunnels and thick walls Jerry was looking out for safety, in the nice, big, dry bedroom he was looking out for comfort. If he could n't have had the safety with the comfort, he would have chosen the safety. But as long as he could have both, he intended to have both.

Higher rose the walls, and presently the bedroom was roofed over. As had been the case in the old house, tiny spaces were left for fresh air to come in and bad air to go out. No one knows better than Jerry how necessary fresh air is no matter how cold the weather. So he took care not to seal the top of his roof with mud so that the air could not pass through. Many nights Jerry worked, and when at last he laid the last stick and the last bulrush in place, he felt that his new house was worth all that he had gone through.

CHAPTER IV

JERRY AND PETER TALK THINGS OVER

Now that his house was finished, Jerry Muskrat felt that he was entitled to a little rest. He had worked long. He had worked hard. He had worked faithfully. Now he could enjoy the results. It certainly was a fine house. Peter Rabbit said so, quite as if he were a judge of houses. You know any old tumble-down house some one else has given up will do for Peter.

"Yes," said Jerry, "it is a pretty good house. It is a better house than my old one. I am glad I have finished it. A house like this means a whole lot of hard work."

"I should say so!" exclaimed Peter. "I would n't work like that for the finest house that ever was."

Jerry Muskrat shook his head at Peter reprovingly. "Peter," said he, "you never look beyond your own nose, do you?"

"Why, of course I do," replied Peter. "If I did n't, how would I ever see anything?"

Jerry laughed. "I did n't mean it just that way," he explained. "I mean you never look ahead and plan for the future. Now you have n't prepared a single thing for the coming winter, have you?"

"No," replied Peter promptly. "Each day brings its own troubles and they are enough, thank you. I don't see any use at all in worrying about things that may never happen. It is time enough to worry when there is something to worry about."

"Who is worrying?" demanded Jerry. "I'm not worrying. It is just to keep from having to worry that I have been working so hard. Now you know, Peter Rabbit, that just as surely as you are sitting here on this bank, you are going to have some mighty hard days if we have a bad winter. You are going to have hard work to get enough to eat. You are going to have hard work to get around in bad weather, and you are going to shiver with the cold."

"Maybe we won't have a bad winter," interrupted Peter.

"Now I," continued Jerry, without heeding the interruption at all, "am going to be perfectly comfortable, no matter what kind of a winter we have. It won't make any difference to me how cold or how stormy the weather may be. It won't make that much difference." Jerry slapped the ground with his tail. "In that house is a nice, soft, comfortable bed of grass. Those walls are so thick the cold will not get through. Jack Frost will freeze the mud in the walls and roof hard. I can swim about under the ice when I please. After I have rested a little, I shall store up a few supplies of food in a storehouse I have provided in the bank. Then Jack Frost may come as soon as he pleases. All winter long I shall live in perfect ease and comfort, and all because I have looked ahead and prepared for it by a little hard work now."

"Huh!" said Peter. Then at a sudden thought he added, "Do you have to lay up a store of food?"

"Oh, no," replied Jerry, "I don't *have* to. Usually I can find enough roots and things in the mud at the bottom of the Smiling Pool."

"Then what do you do it for?" demanded Peter. "That's what I call a waste of time, not to mention the work."

"Nothing of the kind," retorted Jerry. "It is thrift. It is making sure in case I should n't be able to get all I need from the bottom of the Smiling Pool."

"Huh!" said Peter. "Huh! I never do any work I don't have to."

"Which means that you have n't yet learned how to live," laughed Jerry Muskrat.

CHAPTER V

REDDY FOX TRIES TO TEMPT JERRY MUSKRAT

Trust not a fox because he smiles,
Lest it may prove one of his wiles.
Jerry Muskrat.

IF in all the great world there is any one pleasanter than Reddy Fox when he tries to be pleasant, I don't know who it is. Of course, in that handsome red coat of his, he is very good-looking, anyway. Then when he puts on the polite airs that no one knows better than he how to put on, brings into his eyes an innocent look, and smiles, he is as pleasant a fellow as you would care to meet. Only when he forgets and grins a little too broadly, so that he shows all his long teeth, does his face lose its pleasant look.

Now Reddy Fox was one of those who knew all about what was going on in the Smiling Pool. You know Reddy gets his living by knowing what is going on about him. Every night while Jerry Muskrat was at work on that new house, Reddy had stolen over to the Smiling Pool and from among the rushes watched Jerry for a little while and then stolen away again, taking the greatest care not to be seen.

"There isn't the least use in the world trying to get him now," said he, as he thought the matter over. There won't be any use as long as he is at work on that new house. But when he has it finished, he'll begin to think about food for the winter. He'll want very nice things in such a very nice house. I must look around a little. Perhaps I can find some things he will especially like."

Reddy grinned, and the grin was the kind of a grin that showed all his long teeth. He grinned just the same way each night as he trotted away from the Smiling Pool after watching Jerry work. At last came the time when Jerry stopped working, because the house was finished. Reddy knew when Jerry stopped working.

Oh, yes, Reddy knew all about it. He knew that very likely Jerry would take a little vacation before putting in his supplies for the winter. So Reddy was patient and bided his time until he was quite certain that Jerry was beginning to lay up stores of food for winter.

Then one evening Reddy visited the Smiling Pool quite openly. He sat right out on the bank in the moonlight and you could n't imagine anybody more pleasant than was Reddy. He had his most polite airs and his best grin.

"Good evening, neighbor Jerry," said he, and his voice was as pleasant as he knew how to make it.

Jerry stopped swimming long enough to look up at Reddy.

Then, because he could hardly be less polite than Reddy, he squeaked "Good evening" and started on his way. In a minute he dived and disappeared as he swam for the entrance to a certain tunnel in the bank. When he once more popped his head out of water for a breath of fresh air, Reddy was still sitting on the bank right where he had been, and he was just as pleasant as before.

"I have been admiring your house," said Reddy. "You know I travel about a great deal and have seen many houses, but never have I seen one to compare with this. It is wonderful. Not even Paddy the Beaver can build such a house as this."

Now of course this was rank flattery and not the truth at all, for Paddy the Beaver is a master builder, as everybody knows. But it sounded sweet in the ears of Jerry Muskrat, in spite of the fact that he knew Reddy did n't mean a word of it. So he lingered to hear what more Reddy might say.

CHAPTER VI

REDDY'S SMOOTH TONGUE

Whenever there's a fox about,
'Twill pay you well if you watch out.
Jerry Muskrat.

JERRY MUSKRAT was old enough to know better than to stay around listening to Reddy Fox but, like most folks, Jerry likes to be praised and to hear nice things said of him and of his things. When Reddy Fox said that his new house was the finest he had ever seen, and that not even Paddy the Beaver could build such a house, Jerry just could n't take himself away.

"As long as I am out here in the water I am in no danger," thought Jerry, "and Reddy Fox certainly does know a good thing when he sees it. It is a pleasure to listen to one who understands and appreciates things." So Jerry swam around in circles, or idly floated on the surface of the Smiling Pool, while Reddy Fox talked.

Now, as of course you know, and as many of the little people of the Green Meadows and the Green Forest have found out to their sorrow, Reddy Fox has a wonderfully smooth tongue. A smooth tongue, you know, is one that can say all manner of pleasant and delightful things—things to flatter those who listen.

Reddy grinned down at Jerry in the friendliest way. "If I were in your place, Jerry Muskrat," said he, "I certainly would be very proud of such a house as that. I fear I should be rather puffed up about it. You don't seem to be, but if you were, I for one would not blame you in the least. May I ask how many rooms you have in it?"

"One," replied Jerry, wriggling all over with delight at this praise of his skill. "That is, I have just one above water, but it is very large and comfortable. If you like the looks of my house from the outside, you would, I am sure, like it still better if you could see the inside."

"There is n't a doubt of it, Jerry. There is n't a doubt of it," replied Reddy, with great promptness. "I should love to see the inside of it, but I really don't need to, in order to appreciate what a perfectly splendid house it is. If I lived in the water I should certainly want you to build my house for me. In fact, I am not sure but I would like just such a house on land. I think I would, if only knew how to go about building it. Do you suppose I could build one, if I had some one to show me how to do it?"

Jerry Muskrat's eyes shone with pleasure at this praise of his house and his skill. For the time being he quite forget that Reddy Fox was an enemy for whom all his life long he had had to be on the watch. He swam in a little nearer to the bank.

"Do you really mean that you would like a house like mine, only on the land?" he asked.

"I certainly do," replied Reddy. "I can't think of anything I should like as well."

"I—I will be glad to tell you just how to build it," said Jerry, in rather a hesitating way.

Reddy shook his head, still smiling. "I am afraid that would n't do," said he. "In fact, I know it would n't. I never in the world could do it from being told. I should have to have some one to show me. Oh, Jerry, if you would come with me and just show me how to build such a house, I would be the happiest Fox in all the Great World!"

Reddy looked as if he meant every word of it, as indeed he did. A smooth tongue has Reddy Fox — a very smooth tongue.

CHAPTER VII

JERRY WAKES UP JUST IN TIME

When all seems well, with naught to fear,
There may be unseen danger near.

Jerry Muskrat.

NEVER in all his life had Jerry Muskrat been quite so flattered as he was by the admiration of Reddy Fox for his skill as a builder of houses. Listening to the praise which fairly dripped from Reddy's smooth tongue, Jerry actually forgot who was talking. At least, he forgot that Reddy always had been an enemy. It was hard to believe that such a handsome fellow, such a pleasant-spoken fellow, could possibly mean any harm. And he seemed so much in earnest, so very much in earnest when he said that if only Jerry would come with him and show him how to build a house, he would be the happiest Fox in the world, that Jerry had it on the tip of his tongue to say that he would do that very thing and be glad to.

Jerry actually had paddled in to the bank and was beginning to climb out as Reddy said this. And then, as so often happens with a tongue that is too smooth, Reddy's tongue tripped him up. If only he had n't said that Jerry could make him the happiest Fox in the world. That word "Fox" waked Jerry up just in time. He was n't really asleep, you know, but he was so flattered and so interested in what Reddy had said that he had quite forgotten who was talking.

But at the word "Fox" he suddenly realized what he was about to do. In just one wee minute more he would have been right out on the bank, within easy jumping distance of Reddy. Hastily he pushed himself away from the bank and swam far enough out in the Smiling Pool to feel absolutely safe. Then he looked up at Reddy to see if the latter had noticed the haste with which he had left the bank, instead of climbing out on it. He thought there was just a trace of disappointment in Reddy's eyes, but it passed so quickly he could n't be sure.

Apparently Reddy could think of nothing but a new house like Jerry's, only on the land and big enough for him. He went right on talking, just as if he had n't noticed Jerry's action at all.

"If you only could, Jerry Muskrat, if you only could show me how, I believe I could build a house. Anyway, I would be willing to try and to work hard," said he with his eyes half closed, as if trying to picture to himself what such a house would look like. "I certainly would be the envy of everybody on the Green Meadows or in the Green Forest. I believe such a house would tickle Mrs.

Reddy almost to death. I must bring her over here to see your house."

Once more Jerry was growing so interested in the idea of that house that without really knowing it, he was paddling towards the bank. Then as his feet touched bottom, he remembered and made a half-circle to deeper water and there floated lazily.

"I'll be glad to have you bring Mrs. Reddy to see my house," said he. "I am afraid it is n't possible for me to *show* you how to build one, but as I told you before, I will be glad to *tell* you how."

Reddy jumped lightly to his feet. "That will be fine," he replied. "I have an engagement now, but if you have time to spare to-morrow night, I will come over at about this time and we'll talk the idea over. I certainly should like a house like that."

He glanced longingly towards Jerry's new house out in the Smiling Pool, then wishing Jerry good night, trotted away.

CHAPTER VIII

JERRY PLANS A HOUSE FOR REDDY

Suspicion's a persistent thing;
It will not die, but cling and cling.

Jerry Muskrat.

As Reddy Fox trotted away in the moonlight, with never a glance back at the Smiling Pool and Jerry Muskrat, he grinned. On the whole, it was a satisfied grin. "He almost forgot himself," he muttered. "In another minute he would have been out on the bank. If he had, he would have been in my stomach by this time." Reddy chuckled. "I wonder how he came to wake up so suddenly.

Well, I don't mind. I did n't expect to get him the first time. I 'll call a few times and after a while he 'll forget all about who I am."

Promptly at the appointed time the next evening, Reddy appeared on the bank of the Smiling Pool. From the shadows of the Big Rock, Jerry Muskrat was watching for him. He tried to make himself think he was n't watching for Reddy, but he was. And if Reddy had n't come, Jerry would have been disappointed. As it was, he swam out quite as if he were on his way to the entrance of the Laughing Brook.

"Have you my new house all planned for me?" asked Reddy softly.

Jerry stopped swimming and turned towards the bank where Reddy sat. He was looking just as handsome and just as pleasant as he had the night before. Jerry would n't have had Reddy know it for the world, but he had thought of little else but that house since Reddy had left the night before. You know, Jerry dearly loves house-building and planning.

"I 've thought about it a little," he confessed. "Of course, you know my house has n't any entrance except from underneath by way of a tunnel, and that is what makes it so safe," he continued.

Reddy nodded. "I know," said he, "but of course my house, being on dry land, will have to have an entrance in the side."

"No, it won't," cried Jerry Muskrat, drifting in close to the bank. "No, it won't! A doorway in the side would let the cold air in and make it too cold for comfort. Besides, any one who came along could stick his head in. You can have your entrance from a tunnel just the same as I do, only your tunnel will be wholly in the ground and not under water."

Jerry was getting excited as he talked, and he drifted nearer and nearer the bank.

"You have an underground house now, have n't you?" he went on.

"JERRY, YOU CERTAINLY ARE A WONDER!" CRIED REDDY.

Reddy nodded. "I certainly have, and it's a good one," he replied.

"Then all you've got to do is to dig a tunnel from that up to the new house we will build, and there you are!" cried Jerry triumphantly.

"Jerry, you certainly are a wonder!" cried Reddy, pretending to be lost in admiration. "I never, never in the world would have thought of that. No, sir, I never would. I notice that you said the house that *we* will build. I'm so glad you've decided to help me. I can't tell you how grateful I am."

"But I did n't say I would help you build it," cried Jerry, backing away in sudden alarm. "I meant that I would help with the plans and by telling you how."

"Of course," replied Reddy. "How stupid of me not to understand. Now what do you suggest I build that house of?"

Jerry drifted a bit nearer before he replied.

CHAPTER IX

JERRY REMEMBERS SOMETHING

The best of plans will meet defeat
Unless the details are complete.

Jerry Muskrat.

THAT is the reason why so many seemingly splendid plans never amount to anything. The idea may be the finest ever, but it is bound to fail unless each separate detail in it is worked out and made perfect. If one of these little details fails, the whole thing will fail.

Jerry Muskrat, in planning that new house for Reddy Fox, was sure that he had thought of everything. He even had thought of a way for Reddy to get in and out of that house by means of tunnels, just as he himself went in and out of his own house. The only difference would be that Reddy would have dry tunnels instead of tunnels filled with water. He could n't see any reason in the world why Reddy should n't have just as good a house as his, and he said so.

Now, while Reddy Fox pretended to be very much interested in the idea of building a house, he really had n't the least idea of trying to build a house. Of course not. He had no use for such a house, even if he could have built it. Reddy's interest was not at all in the house, but in getting Jerry Muskrat on shore, where it would be a simple matter for Reddy to catch him. But he pretended a tremendous interest in that house, because he hoped that by so doing he could get Jerry to forget there was the least danger, and so induce him to come ashore to show just how that house should be built.

When Reddy asked what Jerry would suggest that the new house be built of, Jerry thought for a minute or two as he drifted in towards the bank of the Smiling Pool where Reddy sat.

"I suppose," said he, "you would have no difficulty in getting plenty of sticks."

"Not the least trouble in the

world," replied Reddy, with a broad grin. "The Green Forest is full of them."

"We could take some rushes from here," continued Jerry thoughtfully, and Reddy grinned more broadly than ever as he noticed that "we."

"Certainly we could," replied Reddy, chuckling down inside, as he saw how Jerry was forgetting everything but the idea of that new house. "I suppose you would cut the rushes for me."

"Of course I would, and be glad to," was Jerry's prompt reply. "With plenty of sticks and rushes, all we would need would be mud to plaster with. This would be to hold them together."

"Did you say mud?" asked Reddy, with a funny look on his face.

Jerry saw that funny look. Then he suddenly remembered that this house was to be built on dry land and if this was to be the case, of course there would be no mud handy. Without mud that house could n't be built. It just *must* have mud. And there must be a lot of it. A little would n't do. But unless Reddy should build his house close to the Smiling Pool — which he was n't in the least likely to do — there would be no way of getting enough mud to it. Jerry looked up at Reddy and in the most mournful voice said:

"All our plans have gone for nothing. You can't build a house like mine. I've just remembered that you haven't any mud. I'm sorry. Let's not talk about it any more."

Without another word, Jerry dived and disappeared.

CHAPTER X

REDDY RETURNS WITH AN IDEA

With most folk it is well agreed
He'll try and try who would succeed.

Jerry Muskrat.

In vain Reddy Fox sat on the bank of the Smiling Pool, waiting for Jerry Muskrat to appear. After a while it became clear to Reddy that Jerry did n't intend to return. He got up and stretched. Then he yawned. He looked down in the Smiling Pool and his face was anything but pleasant. In fact, there was an ugly look on Reddy's face.

"Now what did he have to

think of that mud for?" growled Reddy to himself. "Everything was going fine, until he thought of that mud. He was so interested in the plans for that house for me that in a few minutes more I would have had him out of the Pool to show me what to do and how to do it. Then he remembered that he has to have mud to build a house properly and that ended his interest. I believe he was as disappointed at having to give up the idea of that house as I am at not having him for my dinner. I must think this over. I certainly must."

The next night Reddy was back at the Smiling Pool, just as handsome as ever, just as pleasant as ever, and — if Jerry Muskrat had only known it — just as crafty as ever. He waited some time for Jerry to show himself. You see, having remembered that no house could be built without mud, and that there was no mud to be had where Reddy would want to build a house, Jerry had given up all thought of that house and concluded that Reddy had done the same. So he was n't looking for Reddy to return this night.

As soon as he saw Jerry swimming, Reddy called to him. "Hello, Jerry Muskrat!" he cried. "I've good news. I've thought of a way to get mud for that new house, so we won't have to give up our plans, after all."

In an instant Jerry was all interest. He headed straight towards the bank where Reddy was sitting.

"How are we to get that mud?" he squeaked. "I've thought and thought and thought until my head ached, but the only way I could think of is to carry it from here, and that we can't do."

Reddy grinned. "Listen," said he. "What is mud?"

"Why-why-why, I suppose it is earth and water," stammered Jerry.

"Exactly," replied Reddy. "Certainly. Of course. To be sure. Now, don't you see how we can get all the mud we need?"

Jerry scratched one ear. Then he scratched the other ear. After this he scratched the top of his head. "No-o-o," he replied slowly, "no-o-o, I can't say that I do."

"We'll wait until it rains!" cried Reddy triumphantly. "We'll wait until it rains, and then we will get all the mud we need from the pile of earth I have thrown out in digging my underground house. Wasn't it clever of me to think of that? Now, we won't have to give up the house, after all, and you will help me to build it just as we planned. We'll make it the most wonderful house that ever was!"

For a minute or two Jerry Muskrat brightened up. Then he remembered that what Reddy had thrown out was mostly sand, and sand does not make real mud.

"You'll have to think again, Reddy Fox," said he, and told him why. So once more Reddy went away disappointed.

CHAPTER XI

JERRY HAS OTHER THINGS TO THINK ABOUT

The very time you feel most safe,
And see no reason for alarm,
Is just the time for keeping guard
Against some unexpected harm.
Jerry Muskrat.

REDDY FOX went off to the Old Pasture to put on his thinking cap. Jerry Muskrat just stopped thinking about that house Reddy talked of building. It could n't be built without mud, and how were they to get mud where no mud was! They could n't; so that was all there was about it. It had been great fun to plan that house for Reddy Fox. It had interested him greatly, and he would have dearly loved to help build it. But it could n't be done, and besides, he had other things to think of.

"I 've had rest enough," thought Jerry, the very night he decided that Reddy's house could be no more than a dream. "It is time for me to begin to think about getting some food laid away for the winter. If Reddy Fox ever has a house like mine, he will have to build it without any help from me. I 've wasted all the time on it I 'm going to. It is queer how interested in houses Reddy has become. I never knew him to be before. And, now I think of it he has been wonderfully pleasant. He certainly can be nice when he wants to be. He has n't once tried to catch me. I don't believe that such a thought has even entered his head."

Would n't Reddy have smiled if he could have known what Jerry was thinking? You know and I know that the catching of Jerry was all he was thinking about, and his talk of a house was merely to get Jerry so interested that he would come ashore.

The next night Reddy visited the Smiling Pool just as usual. He could n't keep away. He had n't thought of any way to get mud to build the house, but he hoped to be able to persuade Jerry that they might start the house and trust to luck to get the mud when it was needed. But when he reached the Smiling Pool no Jerry was visible. Reddy waited and waited and waited. At last Jerry appeared, but it was plain to see that he was in a hurry. He merely nodded to Reddy Fox and then dived.

"Well, I never!" exclaimed Reddy, staring at the little circles on the surface of the water made as Jerry dived. "Jerry seems to have something on his mind. I wonder what he is up to now. He might at least have stopped long enough to pass the time of day. I must find out what he is about."

So Reddy waited and waited and waited some more. He managed to hide his impatience, and when at last Jerry climbed out on the Big Rock for a rest, Reddy was just the same pleasant fellow he had been the night before.

"Well, Jerry," he exclaimed, "I thought you had deserted me. I've been waiting ever so long. I thought perhaps you might have thought of some way of building that house without mud."

"I'm sorry, but there is n't any other way," replied Jerry. "If there were, I would n't be able to help you any. I've got too much to do to mind anybody's business but my own. If you want a house, you'll have to get some one else to help build it, or else build it all yourself."

"But what, may I ask, are you so suddenly busy about?" asked Reddy, and tried hard to keep the eagerness from his voice.

"I'm laying up food for the winter," replied Jerry briefly. "Until that is done, I can't think of anything else."

With this he dived from the Big Rock.

CHAPTER XII

REDDY FOX CALLS ON BILLY MINK

Whoe'er is honest with himself,
With others will be honest too.
Remember this where'er you go
And whatsoever you may do.

Jerry Muskrat.

DID you ever try to call on Billy Mink? If so, you know just how difficult it is. Billy is about the hardest person to call on that I know. Of course, it was n't as hard for Reddy Fox as it would have been for you or for me, but even Reddy did n't have an easy time of it. He called a number of times before he found Billy. You see, he did n't know exactly where Billy Mink's home was. Billy had managed to keep that a secret. But he did know some of Billy's favorite places, and it was one of these that Reddy visited over and over again before he even got a glimpse of Billy.

At last, however, he caught a glimpse of Billy, and putting on his most pleasing manner called to him. He knew that if Billy did n't choose to stay, he could vanish in the twinkling of an eye, and he did n't intend to offend Billy if he could help it. It so happened that Billy was engaged in eating a fat trout, so for the time being he actually was quiet.

"Ho, Billy Mink!" called

Reddy, not drawing too near, lest Billy should think his feast was in danger and should run away. "You are just the fellow I want to see."

"Well, here I am. Look at me all you want to," grunted Billy rather ungraciously, between bites. "But don't come any nearer," he added.

Reddy grinned. "I won't," said he. "I won't, although that fish is a great temptation. It's not your fish, but something else I want from you, Billy."

Billy Mink stopped eating long enough to stare at Reddy Fox suspiciously. Seeing that look of suspicion, Reddy chuckled.

"It is just a little information,"

said he. "That is all I want, just a little information. I'm sure you will be willing — quite willing — to give me that."

"That depends on what kind of information you want," retorted Billy, with great promptness. "There are some things I would n't tell you for anything in the world. If it is information about me or any of my affairs, you won't get it. I can tell you that right now. Asking will be just wasting breath."

Reddy chuckled more than ever. "Just as if I did n't know that, Billy Mink!" he exclaimed. "I would n't think of asking you anything personal, because I learned long ago that to do a thing like that would be foolish and a waste of time. I have too much respect for your smartness to try a thing like that, even if I wanted to."

Billy Mink looked pleased, in spite of his efforts not to. You know it pleases most folks to be thought smart. "If that is the case, what is it you want to know?" asked Billy rather more pleasantly.

"I want to know what kind of food Jerry Muskrat eats," replied Reddy. "I know he eats roots, but I want to know what kinds, and what food he is especially fond of. What does he like to store up for winter? Do you know?"

"Of course I know," replied Billy Mink promptly. "It would

be funny if I did n't, seeing as much of him as I do. For one thing, he is very fond of mussels or fresh-water clams. What do you want to know for, anyway?" Billy looked at Reddy suspiciously.

CHAPTER XIII

REDDY FINDS OUT WHAT HE WANTS TO KNOW

Who has attentive ear and eye,
Will learn a lot if he but try.

Jerry Muskrat.

When Billy Mink asked Reddy Fox why he wanted to know what kinds of food Jerry Muskrat liked best, Reddy pretended not to hear. He let his tongue run on just as if he had n't heard that question at all. That is sometimes a handy way of avoiding unpleasant questions that you would rather not answer.

"Now that you mention that

Jerry is fond of mussels, I remember having seen him sitting on the Big Rock, opening them," said Reddy. "It is funny I should n't have remembered that. I've often seen the empty shells in the water where Jerry has been having a feast. Do you eat them, Billy Mink?"

"Not when there are fat trout to be had," laughed Billy, resuming his meal on one and talking between bites. "It is too much work to open those clams. Jerry may have them all, for all I care."

Reddy laughed. "He does n't seem to mind the trouble. I suppose I would n't if that was all the food I had."

"Who said that was all the food

Jerry Muskrat has?" demanded Billy Mink. "Who said that? I certainly did n't. If any one said that, they don't know much about Jerry Muskrat. Those fresh-water clams are only a side dish with Jerry. If he depended on those for all his food, he would n't last long. He would starve."

"How stupid of me!" exclaimed Reddy. "How very stupid of me to make such a remark. Now I think of it, I have often seen Jerry bring up a lily root from the bottom of the Smiling Pool and eat it."

"If you have n't, you 've been blind," declared Billy Mink. "He eats lily roots and other roots growing in the water, and the stems of some of the plants. And he likes other things when he can get them."

"What?" asked Reddy in a very matter-of-fact tone.

"Vegetables from Farmer Brown's garden," replied Billy, grinning broadly. "It is a wonder you have never happened to meet Jerry on his way there or back. If there is any one thing Jerry likes, it 's carrots. He 'll take a long chance to get some."

"Well, we all take long chances to get what we like, don't we?" said Reddy, yawning as if he had quite lost interest in the subject. "It 's a nice day, is n't it? I think I will trot along and look for a dinner. Seeing you enjoy that fish so has made me hungry."

Reddy nodded to Billy Mink and trotted off towards the Green Forest.

Billy Mink stopped eating long enough to watch him out of sight, and on Billy's small brown face was a puzzled frown.

"Now what was that fellow after?" muttered Billy. "What is he so interested in Jerry Muskrat's food for? It is for no good purpose, I'll be bound. I wonder if I said anything I should n't have said. I guess that the next time I see Jerry Muskrat, I'll drop him a hint that Reddy Fox is taking a sudden interest in what he eats."

As for Reddy Fox, he turned as soon as he was out of sight of Billy Mink and with a satisfied chuckle made straight for his home in the Old Pasture. He had found out what he wanted to know, and now he wanted to think it over and plan a little.

CHAPTER XIV

JERRY HAS TWO CALLERS

How few there are who know their neighbors
Their pleasures, fears and joys, and labors.

Jerry Muskrat.

It was very, very early in the morning. It was so early in the morning that some folks would hardly have known it was morning. But it was. Jerry Muskrat, sitting on the Big Rock in the Smiling Pool, knew that it was. He knew that somewhere over behind the Purple Hills jolly, round, red Mr. Sun was kicking off his bedclothes and making ready to show his big red face above the edge of the

Great World, as he began his daily climb up in the blue, blue sky, which did n't seem blue now because of the darkness.

A silver line started out from one bank and made straight toward the Big Rock. Jerry Muskrat saw it. Also, he saw a small brown head at one end of that silver line.

"Hello, Billy Mink. How's the fishing?" squeaked Jerry.

Billy stopped swimming and floated while he talked. "Hello, Jerry," he replied. "I thought I'd find you here. It would n't seem like the Big Rock not to find you sitting on it at this hour. Fishing is good, thank you. That reminds me that Reddy Fox happened along yesterday and seemed to be taking a great interest in you."

"It's my new house," explained Jerry. "That's what Reddy is so interested in."

"Oh, is it?" There was something very like surprise in Billy Mink's voice. "I thought it was your food. He did n't mention house to me. Well, I must get on. I think I'll go down to the Big River and see what is going on."

The silver line with the little brown head at the end of it moved swiftly across the Smiling Pool and vanished down the Laughing Brook. Jerry Muskrat thoughtfully pulled his whiskers. "That's funny," said he to himself. "That certainly is funny.

Reddy has never mentioned food to me. I wonder——"

But just what Jerry wondered no one will ever know, for who should appear on the bank of the Smiling Pool just then but Reddy Fox himself.

"How's the little worker getting on with filling his storehouse?" asked Reddy.

"Not as well as he is going to be in about two minutes," replied Jerry, rather shortly, and with a splash dived from the Big Rock. He was gone for quite a while, during which time he dug up and carried to his storehouse three particularly fine roots. Then, being tired, he once more climbed out on the Big Rock, and the very first thing he saw was Reddy Fox just where he had last seen him. Reddy did n't look as if he had moved.

"I 've been waiting for you, Jerry. You were gone a long time," said he.

"I did n't know you were waiting," replied Jerry. "I guess it would n't have made any difference if I had, because these days I have too much to do to gossip. Winter will soon be here, and I 've a lot to get done before then." To hear him, you would have thought that he had so much to do that he could n't sit still a minute.

"Oh, it does n't matter," replied Reddy. "I have time enough to spare. I just wanted to say to you that last night I discovered some of the finest carrots that I have ever laid my eyes on, and knowing that you like them, I thought of you right away, and how perhaps you might like some to put away for the winter."

Right away Jerry was interested.

CHAPTER XV

REDDY'S INVITATION

A purpose you will always find
In everything, unless you're blind.
Jerry Muskrat.

THE mere mention of carrots always makes Jerry Muskrat's mouth water. Yes, Sir, it does just that. You see, it is this way: Carrots to Jerry are very much like some rare fruit to you, something that you can get only once in a while. Jerry never feels thoroughly at home on land, you know. He wants to be close to the water. So it is only once in a great while that he travels any distance on land.

Now, of course, it is n't often that one finds carrots near the Laughing Brook or the Smiling Pool. When they are found there, it usually is wisest to try to forget all about them, because — can you guess why? Because there is very likely to be a trap close at hand. As Jerry gained wisdom and learned about traps, in the days before Farmer Brown's Boy had stopped all trapping along the Laughing Brook and the Smiling Pool, he had learned how to get the bait sometimes without being caught, and so he had learned the taste of carrots. Several times he had been bold enough to go way over to Farmer Brown's garden down on the Green Meadows to look for carrots, but he had always been disappointed. Other good things he had found, but no carrots.

Thus it was that when Reddy Fox told him that he, Reddy, had discovered some of the finest carrots that ever grew, Jerry was interested. Of course. How could he help it?

"Did you say carrots?" asked Jerry, quite as if he was n't sure that his ears had n't played him a trick.

"I certainly did," replied Reddy Fox. "I certainly said carrots. They are the finest carrots I ever have laid my two eyes on, and in my travels I have seen a great many carrots. I don't eat carrots myself, but it is a fact that just looking at those carrots, Jerry, and thinking how much one who does eat them would enjoy them, made me hungry. Then I thought of you."

Jerry did n't see the sly wink in one of Reddy's eyes as he said this.

"Yes," continued Reddy, "I thought of you and came straight over here to tell you about them. I remembered what you said about laying up stores for winter, and it came to me that perhaps you would like to put some of these carrots away with the other good things. I certainly would, if I liked carrots."

Jerry Muskrat's mouth watered more than ever as he listened. It watered so that Reddy Fox saw it water, and turned away to hide a grin.

"Did you say that those carrots are very far from here?" asked Jerry wistfully.

"I did n't say," replied Reddy. "Do you know where Farmer Brown's garden is?"

Jerry nodded. "Yes," said he. "At least, I know where his corn-field is."

"Well," replied Reddy promptly, "those carrots are there. They are right at the end of that corn-field, the end nearest the Smiling Pool. There are rows and rows of them. I tell you what, Jerry; I have n't anything special to do this evening, and I will be delighted to show you the way there and help you bring back some of those carrots. Nothing could give me greater pleasure. Now, don't say a word. I'll be over here shortly after the Black Shadows appear, and we'll go over there together. I just won't take no for an answer. It will be the joy of my life to help you get those carrots."

"Thank you, it is ever so kind of you," replied Jerry, trying to be polite, and not knowing what else to say. "I'll be right here watching for you, as soon as the Black Shadows come to-night."

"I won't keep you waiting long," replied Reddy, as he turned and trotted off.

CHAPTER XVI

JERRY TAKES A DAYLIGHT JOURNEY

To fool another through and through,
Just let him think he's fooling you.

Jerry Muskrat.

SEATED on the Big Rock in the Smiling Pool as the Black Shadows were chased away by the Jolly Little Sunbeams and daylight took the place of darkness, Jerry Muskrat watched Reddy Fox trot off across the Green Meadows towards the Old Pasture. Reddy looked back just once and smiled. At least, he meant to smile. What he really did do was to grin.

If Jerry had been near enough

to see that grin clearly, he would have seen in it such slyness and eagerness as might have given him an uncomfortable feeling. As it was that grin looked pleasant, which was what Reddy fully intended.

"It was wonderfully good of Reddy Fox to come way over here just to tell me about those carrots," thought Jerry, "and to invite me to go with him to get some. He must think a lot of me to go to all that trouble. He certainly must. He—"

Jerry stopped right there and suddenly sat up very straight, while a funny look crossed his face. He pulled his whiskers thoughtfully, and the look on his face grew still funnier. "I wonder," said Jerry very softly, talking to himself, "I wonder if he was thinking more of me or more of himself. I wonder if it was n't his own stomach and not my stomach that put the idea of carrots into his head. Nothing would give him more pleasure than to show me the way — inside his stomach! Perhaps I 'm not fair to you, Reddy Fox, but I can't afford to take any chances. I 'm going to start for that garden of Farmer Brown's this very minute. It may be risky to do it in broad daylight, but I am afraid it would be a whole lot riskier to do it after dark with you, Mr. Fox. I would n't do it at all, if it was n't that it just seems as if I *must* have some of those carrots."

Jerry looked this way and looked

that way and looked the other way, until he was quite sure that Redtail the Hawk was nowhere to be seen. Then Jerry dived into Smiling Pool and swam quickly across it and up the Laughing Brook. At a certain place a little ditch came into it, a ditch which had been dug to drain off the water from the Green Meadows in the spring. The grass grew long on both sides and hung over the little ditch. Jerry turned into this little ditch, which was now quite dry, and ran along it, keeping as much under the grass as he could. It led straight in the direction of Farmer Brown's cornfield, on one side of which were rows and rows of delicious carrots, according to Reddy Fox.

It was a long way to the end of that ditch. Anyway, it was long to Jerry Muskrat, who does little traveling on land. It was a real journey for Jerry. When he reached the end of the ditch, he came to another ditch going crosswise. He turned down this a little way and then very carefully climbed up the bank until he could peep over. He was now almost on the edge of the cornfield, on the very side where Reddy had said the carrots were.

CHAPTER XVII

BLACKY THE CROW DROPS A HINT

The one whose knowledge is complete
  I never yet have met.
The more one gains possession of,
  The more he 'll try to get.

Jerry Muskrat.

REDDY Fox sat on his doorstep in the Old Pasture, feeling very fine, very fine indeed. In the first place, he had had a splendid sleep. All the long sunny morning Reddy had slept, for he had been out all the night before. Now it was afternoon and Reddy was taking a sunbath, a thing he dearly loves to do at times. And while he took that sunbath, he was dreaming. He was dreaming daydreams, and they were very pleasant daydreams. He was dreaming of eating. Did you ever have that kind of daydreams? Then you know just how pleasant Reddy's dreams were.

There was only one thing wrong with those dreams. That was that they made Reddy impatient. He just could n't help being impatient. In the first place he was hungry; in the second place, he knew, or thought he knew, exactly what kind of a dinner he would have as soon as shadow-time arrived. He would have a Muskrat dinner, and the very thought of it made his mouth water and water. That is why he was impatient — impatient for the coming of shadow-time.

Aside from this impatience, Reddy was perfectly happy. He had tried all sorts of ways to get Jerry Muskrat up on land where he could be caught, but always without success. But this coming night it would be different. Jerry had promised to be waiting for him at the Smiling Pool after the coming of the Black Shadows. Then together they would start for Farmer Brown's garden, where were growing the rows and rows of carrots Jerry Muskrat is so fond of. They would start to get Jerry a dinner. At least, that is what Jerry would think. But they would get a dinner for Reddy instead. Jerry himself would furnish that dinner, just as soon as he was once out of the water.

"He does n't suspect a thing," thought Reddy. "It 's funny how stupid some folk can be, but it is well for me that they are stupid. If Jerry Muskrat really was smart at all, he would n't have listened to me. He would have known what I was trying to do. But his appetite was too much for his wits. Jerry is like a lot of others — ruled by his stomach instead of his head, which is very fine for me. Hello, here comes Blacky the Crow! I wonder if he has any news this afternoon."

Sure enough, there was Blacky, coming from the direction of the

Green Meadows. When he saw Reddy sitting on his doorstep, he stopped in the top of a little tree near by to pass the time of day.

"What's the news?" asked Reddy.

"Just what I was going to ask you," replied Blacky, who is a crafty black rascal and seldom is to be caught napping.

Reddy grinned good-naturedly. "There is n't a thing to tell you," he replied. "I have been asleep ever since daylight, and you are the first person I have seen."

"And I," replied Blacky, "can tell you little more, except that I saw Jerry Muskrat a long way from the Smiling Pool."

Reddy jumped as if a sharp

thorn had suddenly pricked him. "What's that you said?" he exclaimed.

"I said that I saw Jerry Muskrat a long way from the Smiling Pool," replied Blacky. "He was way over towards Farmer Brown's cornfield."

"Excuse me," exclaimed Reddy, rising hurriedly. "I have suddenly remembered an appointment which I had quite forgotten. I should like to stay for a chat, but this matter is so important that I must attend to it at once. You understand how it is, don't you?"

"Perfectly," replied Blacky. "Don't let me detain you for a moment." Then he spread his black wings and flew away chuckling.

You see, he had n't told Reddy that when he saw Jerry it was some time before, and Jerry was then well on his way home.

CHAPTER XVIII

JERRY MUSKRAT APOLOGIZES

Who ventures nothing, nothing gains;
While boldness often much obtains.

Jerry Muskrat.

THE eyes of Blacky the Crow twinkled and snapped and snapped and twinkled as he watched Reddy Fox hurry from the Old Pasture down across the Green Meadows towards Farmer Brown's cornfield. Then Blacky chuckled and haw-hawed and caw-cawed as he flew over to the Green Forest.

"Jerry Muskrat must be back to the Smiling Pool by this time, and Reddy will have his hurry and trouble for nothing," chuckled Blacky.

It was just as Blacky thought. Reddy hurried with all his might, and when Reddy really hurries he can get over the ground very fast indeed. He hurried with all his might until he was near the end of Farmer Brown's cornfield, where the rows of carrots were. Then he slowed down to a walk. To have seen him you would have thought he was just out walking for his health, with nothing at all on his mind. You see, he did n't want to frighten Jerry Muskrat, if it should be that Jerry was anywhere about.

So Reddy walked along between the rows, and all the time his keen glances were darting this way and that way and not missing a single little thing. You can guess how he hoped to see a brown form very busy among them. But he did n't see anything of the kind. In fact, he did n't see anything unusual until he was almost to the corner nearest a certain drainage ditch. There was a gap in the outside row of green carrot tops. Reddy looked sharply all about, but no one was in sight. Then he lightly jumped over two or three rows of green carrot tops until he came to the gap in the outside row.

"Ha!" exclaimed Reddy, and in his voice were both disappointment and anger. At that gap in the row some one had been digging. Some one had dug up the carrots which had grown there. Reddy sniffed all about the place, and on his face was a look not at all pleasant to see. His nose told him that the digger of those carrots was none other than Jerry Muskrat. Also, it told him how Jerry had followed that ditch to get there.

Reddy started along the bank of that ditch at a gallop, but as he drew near the Laughing Brook and saw that Jerry must have reached it in safety, he stopped. He was far too crafty to show himself. Instead, he turned and trotted back to the Old Pasture.

Just after the coming of the Black Shadows that evening,

Reddy appeared on the bank of the Smiling Pool. On the Big Rock sat Jerry Muskrat.

"Good evening, Jerry," said Reddy pleasantly. "Are you ready to go with me for those delicious carrots I told you about?"

Jerry shifted about uneasily before he finally found his tongue. "I-I'm sorry to disappoint you, Reddy," he stammered, "but I've already been there and found the carrots, and I'm too tired to go again. You see, after you told me about them, I got to thinking of them until I could n't think of another thing, and I just *had* to go. I hope you don't mind."

"Not at all! Not at all!" replied Reddy pleasantly, though

black anger was in his heart. "We can go together some other time. You will need a great many of those carrots for winter, and I can help you bring them here. By sun-up to-morrow morning you will be quite rested. What do you say if I meet you here then?"

"Fine," replied Jerry. "I'll be right here."

CHAPTER XIX

JERRY IS TRUE TO HIS WORD

Whate'er you do, I pray that you
May to your word be always true.

Jerry Muskrat.

JERRY MUSKRAT believes that when he has given his word to do a thing, he should do that thing. He had given his word that he would be right there on the Big Rock at sun-up the next morning. He had given his word to Reddy Fox, and he fully intended to keep it.

With this Reddy had to be content. In his own mind he was doubtful if Jerry would keep it.

You see, Reddy Fox is one whose word is not to be trusted. I am sorry to say so, but it is true. Being untruthful himself, he always doubts the truthfulness of others. It usually is that way with untruthful people.

But there was nothing Reddy could do but be patient and hope that Jerry would be on the Big Rock at sun-up the next morning, ready to go with him for carrots in Farmer Brown's garden. Reddy would have liked to stay and watch Jerry all through the night, but he could n't do that. In the first place, Jerry might discover what he was doing and then he would be sure to suspect something. In the second place, Reddy just had to get something to eat. He just *had* to go hunt for a meal.

All that night, while he hunted on the Green Meadows for Meadow Mice and in the Green Forest for Wood Mice, his thoughts were over at the Smiling Pool, wondering what Jerry Muskrat was about. He did n't suspect Jerry of having outwitted him the day before. It did n't enter his head that Jerry had suspected him and that that was the real reason he had gone for those carrots in broad daylight. He thought it was just because Jerry wanted them so much that he simply could n't wait. You see, he always thought of Jerry Muskrat as rather a stupid fellow, despite the fact that Jerry always had managed to keep from being caught. Very smart people are that way sometimes. They admire their own smartness so much that they fail to see smartness in others.

A little before sun-up, Reddy crept to a place where he could peep out over the Smiling Pool to the Big Rock. Without a sound Reddy lay there with his eyes fixed on the Big Rock. After what seemed ages, the Black Shadows began to creep away and presently jolly, round, red Mr. Sun began his daily climb up into the blue, blue sky. Then a dark head suddenly bobbed up in the Smiling Pool, and there was Jerry Muskrat swimming straight to the Big Rock. Reddy grinned. Jerry had kept his word.

There was no longer any doubt in Reddy's mind.

Reddy crept back until he was sure that when he stood up he could n't be seen by Jerry. Then he trotted forward to the Smiling Pool, as if he had been hurrying to keep that appointment.

"Good morning," said he pleasantly. "I see you are all ready to go with me for those carrots."

CHAPTER XX

REDDY BEGINS TO SUSPECT

Investigate and for yourself find out
Those things which most you want to
know about. *Jerry Muskrat.*

THE sight of Jerry Muskrat sitting on the Big Rock in the Smiling Pool was a great relief to Reddy Fox. You see, he had been afraid that Jerry would n't be there as he had agreed to be. But he was there and that could mean but one thing — that he was ready to go for those carrots. So Reddy's greeting was very pleasant and hearty.

For a minute Jerry Muskrat

did n't reply, and when he did he mumbled. He mumbled very much as if his mouth was filled with something. Then he swallowed hastily and after this his voice was quite clear.

"I'm sorry to disappoint you, Reddy Fox," said he, "but I've decided not to go for those carrots to-day. It is mighty good of you to come over here and offer to go with me to help bring those carrots back (Jerry turned his head to hide a knowing grin), but I could n't think of imposing on you like that. Besides, you know, I seldom travel far on land in broad daylight."

"But you went in broad daylight yesterday," protested Reddy, trying hard to hide his disappointment.

"Which is the very best reason why I don't want to go to-day," replied Jerry promptly.

"Then why did n't you say so last evening, instead of saying that you would go with me this morning? I always supposed the word of Jerry Muskrat was to be trusted. Now I know it is n't worth anything at all," retorted Reddy bitterly.

"Hold on, Neighbor Fox! Hold on!" cried Jerry. "Just rub up your memory a little bit. I did n't say a word about going with you for those carrots. All I agreed was to be right here at sun-up this morning, and here I am. If there is any one thing I pride myself on, it is in being true to my word. I really had other business to attend to, but I said I would be here and here I am. Now if you will excuse me, I'll be going. Come again when I'm not so busy."

With this Jerry dived into the Smiling Pool, and Reddy did n't suspect that he had been outwitted by Jerry Muskrat. He thought things had just happened so, and that Jerry had no idea that he, Reddy, was other than the friend he pretended to be. And then he caught sight of something Jerry had left on the Big Rock. It was the tip of a carrot.

Reddy stared and stared, and as he stared, suspicion grew. "I believe," he muttered, "that Jerry Muskrat went over to that field last night after all, and got some more carrots and that is why he does n't want to go to-day. I wonder if it can possibly be that he suspects me. I begin to believe that he does." Reddy ground his teeth in rage.

"I'll get him yet!" he snarled. "I'll get him yet! No Muskrat can go about bragging that he is smarter than Reddy Fox. I'll show him! I'll show him!" With this Reddy trotted off home, to try to think of a plan to outwit Jerry Muskrat.

CHAPTER XXI

JERRY PLAYS A DANGEROUS GAME

To be too sure is a mistake
The smartest folk will sometimes make.

Jerry Muskrat.

IF Jerry Muskrat had seen what a rage Reddy Fox had gone off in, he might have felt a little nervous. But he did n't see because, you remember, he had dived into the Smiling Pool and disappeared himself. He had gone straight to his new house, and there, in his snug chamber, he lay chuckling to himself as he thought of how he had fooled Reddy a second time and had secured some of those fine carrots. And he had been quite honest about it too. He had n't broken his word or told an untruth.

When Reddy had visited him the evening before and invited him to go for carrots, Jerry had been entirely truthful when he said that he was too tired to think of such a thing. So Reddy had left, promising to return at sun-up. Now it does n't take the little people of the Green Forest long to rest, even when they are very tired, and the night was n't half gone when Jerry felt as good as ever. So, what did he do but go for more carrots, feeling sure that Reddy Fox would not suspect him and so would not be over where the carrots grew. He had reached home again only just in time to keep his word and be on the Big Rock at sun-up.

"Unless he is more stupid than he has the name of being, Reddy will begin to suspect something," thought Jerry. "I've fooled him twice now, and he isn't the kind of fellow to be fooled right along. I suppose the sensible thing for me to do is to be content with the carrots I've got. But, dear me, when I think of all the carrots over there, and the few I have here, it is more than I can stand. I simply must have some more."

For a little while Jerry lay quiet, trying to forget carrots and be content. But he couldn't do it. No, Sir, he couldn't do it. He had a little nap, but during that nap he dreamed of carrots. He dreamed of a great pile of carrots all about him, so that all he had to do was to reach out and help himself. That dream was too much for Jerry. When he awoke he just could n't resist temptation any longer. He must have one more try at those carrots, anyway.

"I'll go right this minute," he declared. "To be sure, it is broad daylight, but I've been there once before in broad daylight. Reddy Fox won't suspect me of going this morning. He knows I went last night, and he will think I will want to sleep all the morning. Besides, he has been out all night himself, and the chances are he will go home now for a little sleep himself.

Along in late afternoon he 'll be on watch over near those carrots. It won't be safe to go then, nor will it be safe to go in the night. I suppose I am playing a dangerous game when I try to outwit Reddy Fox, but I 'm going to try it this once."

So Jerry started once again for the field where the carrots grew in rows and rows, and while he worked Reddy Fox slept.

CHAPTER XXII

JERRY MUSKRAT'S GREAT IDEA

Ideas are very funny things;
At least I think them so.
From nothing out of nowhere they
Just seem to come, you know.

Jerry Muskrat.

WHEN you have done a thing once, it is always easier to do it again. A thing which seems dangerous the first time you do it seems a little less dangerous the second time, if nothing happened the first time. Jerry had made one successful trip in broad daylight to Farmer Brown's field where the carrots grew in rows and rows. So now, as he started to make the trip again, it did n't seem nearly as dangerous as it had the first time.

As before, Jerry kept in the drainage ditches. With the long grass hanging over them as it did, they were almost as good as tunnels. He felt that it would be only by chance that he would be discovered there. The real danger would be when he had to leave the shelter of the ditch nearest the place where the carrots grew and run out in the open. When he reached this point, Jerry poked his head up very cautiously and looked this way and looked that way, and studied and studied to make sure that the way was clear and no one was near enough to see him.

Just as he made up his mind that it was safe for him to run across to where the carrots were, a harsh voice caused him to duck down quickly. "Caw, caw!" said the voice. Jerry crouched down under the overhanging grass. He did n't want to be seen by Blacky the Crow. Not that he was afraid of Blacky. Blacky himself could n't hurt him and would n't try. But Blacky's tongue was dangerous. If Blacky should see him, it would be quite like Blacky to tell Reddy Fox or Old Man Coyote. So the surest and wisest thing to do was to hide until Blacky was nowhere about.

It was as he crouched there in that little ditch under the overhanging grass, hiding from Blacky the Crow, that the great idea came to Jerry. It came so suddenly that he nearly squealed aloud. It was such a splendid, such a perfectly splendid idea, that he fairly hugged himself.

"Why did n't I think of it before? Why did n't I think of it before?" he kept saying over and over. "It is the simplest thing ever was. Now, I 'll have all the carrots I can eat, and I'll be perfectly safe while getting them. Reddy Fox will never in the world find out about it, and if he should, it would n't do him the least bit of good. It is simply great. I wonder how I came to think of it."

What was Jerry's great idea?

It was to dig a tunnel from the bottom of that ditch right over to where the carrots were and make an opening right among them. Then he could make a little storeroom leading off the tunnel and pack it full of carrots. Simple, was n't it?

CHAPTER XXIII

JERRY GETS RIGHT DOWN TO HARD WORK

The greatest joy in all the world is work,
Just work.
Who will not do his honest share's a shirk,
Plain shirk.
Jerry Muskrat.

THAT is a fact. It may seem queer to you, but it is a fact that the greatest joy in the world is found in good honest work, and some day you 'll find it out. The busiest people in the world are usually the happiest.

Now, digging a tunnel is n't the easiest work ever was. It is n't easy even for Jerry Muskrat, who, as you know, is a very good digger. Jerry could think of lots of things easier than digging. But he would n't think of them. Instead, he kept in his mind all the time the thought of carrots and the joy of eating all he wanted of them.

And so, as he dug, Jerry was happy. He was too busy to be anything else. He started his tunnel at a point where the overhanging grass was longest and thickest. You see, he did n't want anybody to discover the entrance. The earth he dug out he scattered about on the bottom of the ditch. It did n't take him very long to dig himself in out of sight. As soon as he had done this, he felt easier in his mind. He felt quite safe. All that day

Jerry dug and dug, with short rests between. When the Black Shadows crept out from the Purple Hills across the Green Meadows, to where the carrots grew in rows and rows, Jerry crept out of that little ditch, ran over and dug up a couple of carrots and took them back to his tunnel. There he ate them. Then he curled up for a nap, for he had worked so hard he was very tired.

While he slept, Reddy Fox trotted along right over his head. Jerry did n't know it. Neither did Reddy. Reddy had first visited the Smiling Pool. Of course, he had seen nothing of Jerry there. Then he had hurried straight to Farmer Brown's field, where the carrots grew in rows and rows. All the way there he had watched for Jerry Muskrat. When he had reached there, he tip-toed up and down the rows, hoping to surprise Jerry feasting there. At length he found where Jerry had dug the two carrots early that evening. He had followed Jerry's tracks to the little drainage ditch and on the bank of that he had stopped. There was a little water in the bottom of that ditch, and Reddy does not like to wet his feet if he can avoid it. Besides, he knew that he could no longer follow Jerry's tracks down there. There were no tracks in the water and no scent.

So Reddy ground his teeth and snarled in disappointment and then he set out to follow along the little ditch in the hope that somewhere along it he would find Jerry Musk-rat on his way home. Knowing nothing of this, Jerry awoke by and by and at once went to work again.

CHAPTER XXIV

REDDY FOX IS STARTLED

Don't blame the fox; he has to live;
But to him no advantage give.

Jerry Muskrat.

JERRY MUSKRAT had n't been so tickled with himself — with his own smartness — since he had finished that fine new house in the Smiling Pool. Never since he could remember had he taken more real pleasure in work than he did in the digging of this tunnel he was at work on — the tunnel from a certain drainage ditch to that part of Farmer Brown's garden where were rows and rows of splendid carrots.

"Jerry," said he to himself as he worked, "you are a very clever fellow. You certainly are a very clever fellow. You are going to have all the carrots you want for the winter, in spite of the fact that they grow a long way from the Smiling Pool, and you are going to get them with very little risk. Yes, you certainly are clever."

All the time Jerry kept right on digging, stopping only to eat and sleep. He wasted no time. Jerry is a great believer in thrift, and he knows that wasting time is one of the worst kinds of thriftlessness. Jerry is one of those wise persons who once having started a thing keeps at it until it is finished. So the tunnel grew and grew, until at last Jerry felt sure that he must be right under those delicious carrots which were growing in rows and rows. So he began to dig up and presently he popped right out of the ground just where he wanted to — amongst the carrots. Then, far enough back to be quite safe, he dug a snug little storeroom just to one side and connected with the tunnel.

All this time Reddy Fox had been growing worse and worse in his temper. You will remember it was he who had first told Jerry about those carrots. Reddy remembered it too, and every time he thought of it he ground his teeth. Every time he visited those carrots he saw where Jerry Muskrat had dug some up. He was sure that Jerry got to the cornfield by means of the little drainage ditches which Farmer Brown had dug long ago to drain his land of water, when there was too much, and carry it off to the Laughing Brook.

At first he thought it would be an easy matter to catch Jerry. All he would have to do would be to watch at a place in the drainage ditch where there was no overhanging grass. Jerry would have to pass there, and then all he, Reddy, would need to do would be to spring right down on Jerry's back. So he found just such a place and then lay down on the bank and watched and watched. He watched

THE SIGHT WAS SO UNEXPECTED THAT IT ACTUALLY STARTLED REDDY.

in the night and he watched in the daytime, but never once did he catch so much as a glimpse of Jerry Muskrat. You see, this was during the time that Jerry was digging that tunnel, and so he did n't go back to his home in the Smiling Pool.

Then, one moonlight night after watching until his patience was at an end, Reddy trotted over to the place where the carrots grew, and there in the moonlight between two rows sat Jerry Muskrat. The sight was so unexpected that it actually startled Reddy. It startled him so that he made a little noise. Jerry turned and saw him.

CHAPTER XXV

REDDY FOX LOSES HIS HEAD

Who, startled by a great surprise,
Controls his tongue is very wise.

Jerry Muskrat.

OF course, Reddy Fox did n't really lose his head. If he had, that would have been the end of him, and I for one would have felt bad. We could n't get along without Reddy Fox, despite his sly ways and the mischief he gets into. When folks are very much excited and do things without stopping to think, — foolish things, — they are said to have lost their heads.

That is what happened to Reddy Fox, when he was so surprised that he was actually startled by discovering Jerry Muskrat sitting between two rows of carrots in the moonlight. If he had n't lost his head, he would n't have given himself away as he did. You remember that all along he had pretended to be the friend of Jerry Muskrat. He had pretended that all in the world he cared about was to help Jerry get those carrots. But now he quite lost his usual cunning. Without stopping to think, he snarled and sprang straight at Jerry.

The very instant he had done it, Reddy knew that he had made a sad mistake. He knew that he had shown his true feelings, and that never again could he hope to make Jerry think him friendly. Reddy had lost his head, and the knowledge that he had, made him lose it still more. It often works that way.

The instant Jerry discovered Reddy, he ducked under the spreading tops of the nearest carrots and ran, keeping as much under them and in the Black Shadows as he could. Perhaps you think he ran straight for the opening to his tunnel. He did n't. He did n't do anything of the kind. He headed for that nearest little ditch. He had no intention of showing Reddy that opening among the carrots.

Now, clumsy as he looks, Jerry can move fast for a short distance. He did now. Reddy plunged after him. Instead of trusting to his nose, he trusted to his eyes, for as I told you, he had quite lost his head. The only way he could tell where Jerry ran was by the movement of the carrot-tops as Jerry darted under them. This was all right until the Merry Little Breezes, who were out for a moonlight frolic, saw what was going on and hastened to help Jerry by making all the carrot-tops wave. Then Reddy could n't tell which were moved by Jerry and which by the Merry Little Breezes. He had to stop short.

Then he remembered the ditch.

"That's where he's gone, of course," thought Reddy. "He'll start for home as fast as his legs will take him, and somewhere along that ditch I'll catch him."

Full of this idea, off raced Reddy to the drainage ditch, and at once began to hurry along the bank towards the Laughing Brook,—all the time watching and sniffing for signs of Jerry Muskrat. He was halfway to the Laughing Brook before he stopped to get his wits to working. He had neither seen nor smelled Jerry, and it was very queer.

CHAPTER XXVI

REDDY DISCOVERS WHAT BECAME OF JERRY

Whate'er he does, where'er he goes,
A Fox will always trust his nose.

Jerry Muskrat.

As a rule there is nothing stupid about Reddy Fox. He may be fooled now and then, but he soon finds it out, and he is n't likely to be fooled twice in the same way. When he is fooled, it is more often by himself than by anybody else. He fools himself by not giving other folks credit for being as smart as they are.

That is the way it had been

with Jerry Muskrat. Reddy had made the mistake of not thinking Jerry as smart as he is, and so had not suspected Jerry of even trying to fool him. Now, however, Reddy had his eyes open. It had come over him that if he was to catch Jerry, he would have to use his wits for all they were worth.

"Here I am halfway to the Laughing Brook, and I have n't caught so much as a whiff of the scent of Jerry Muskrat," muttered Reddy, as he stopped to look down in the little drainage ditch along which he had felt sure Jerry had run. He went on a little farther until he came to a place where the grass did not overhang the ditch, and where the bottom of it was quite dry. "Now, I'll make sure," muttered Reddy, as he jumped down in the ditch.

Very carefully he sniffed all about in the bottom of the ditch. There was n't a trace, not a teeniest, weeniest trace of Jerry Muskrat. Jerry could n't have passed that way. He could n't possibly have run along there and not left a little scent.

"Ha!" snarled Reddy, jumping out of the ditch. "He has n't gone back home. He is somewhere between here and the field where the carrots are." He looked long and eagerly up the ditch, as if trying to make up his mind. Then once again he jumped down in the ditch. "I hate to get my feet wet, but I'm not going to take any chances this time," he muttered. "If Jerry Muskrat is anywhere in here, I'll find him."

With this Reddy started back along the bottom of the ditch, pushing under the overhanging grass, and all the time using his wonderful nose for all it was worth. It was n't until he reached the little cross-ditch at the end of the ditch he had been following, that he found a trace of Jerry. Then he found where Jerry had scrambled down into the ditch. His nose told him that.

Reddy felt better. He knew that now he was on the right track and at once he hurried on. And so it was that presently Reddy came to the entrance to Jerry's tunnel in the bank. He knew now where Jerry was.

CHAPTER XXVII

WISDOM OVERCOMES ANGER

The one thing in the world of strife
More precious than all else is life.

Jerry Muskrat.

WHEN Reddy Fox discovered what had become of Jerry Muskrat, he straightway lost his temper. Of all foolish things in this world, nothing is quite so foolish as losing one's temper. Sometimes it is hard work not to, however. Then the only thing to do is to get over it as quickly as possible.

When Reddy found that hole at the end of the drainage ditch and knew that it was in this way that

Jerry Muskrat had so fooled him, he flew into such a rage that he ground his teeth and made ugly-sounding little snarls down in his throat. Without stopping to really think, he sprang forward with the idea of digging Jerry out. He was so angry that he felt he must do something.

Just in time common sense whispered to him, "You know well enough that you can't dig him out, so what is the use of trying?"

Reddy paused and tried to swallow his anger. "That is perfectly true," muttered Reddy. "There is no knowing how far that tunnel goes. Besides, it is very wet down here, and I would get myself all muddy for nothing. The thing for me to do is not to let Jerry Muskrat know that I have found out about this hole of his. Then all I will have to do will be to watch it; sooner or later I will catch him. He is in there now, and he will have to come out sometime. A little patience, a little watchful waiting, is all that is necessary. I think, Mr. Jerry Muskrat, that this is the time I have you."

Reddy jumped up on the bank and chose a comfortable place where he could lie down, yet keep his eyes fixed on the entrance to Jerry Muskrat's tunnel. He was quite sure that Jerry could not possibly see him, even if he were suspicious and looked all around before coming out. The longer he lay there, the more pleased he felt that he had not let his temper get the best of him and so give him away. Wisdom had overcome temper and Reddy was glad of it. He knew right down in his heart that his chances of success were much greater than they would have been had he foolishly tried to dig Jerry out.

All the time Jerry Muskrat was snug and safe in the little chamber, way up in the bank where he had begun to store away the carrots which he had stolen from Farmer Brown's garden. He did n't know he had stolen them, so he should n't be blamed for that. You see, the little people of the Green Meadows and the Green Forest think they have a right to whatever they may find that somebody else has not already taken. So when they take things from gardens and orchards, they do not know that they are stealing. Please remember this, if they ever bother you in this way.

CHAPTER XXVIII

SAMMY JAY BECOMES INQUISITIVE

Patience in a cause that's good
Becomes a virtue, as it should.
Jerry Muskrat.

YOU know what it is to be inquisitive. Of course you do. Most folks are inquisitive at times. It means trying to find out about things, — particularly things which may not concern you. It is just another name for Peter Rabbit's dreadful curiosity. Sammy Jay is one of the most inquisitive people I know of. Sammy cannot bear to have anything going on that he does n't know about. If there is anything at all suspicious-looking, Sammy promptly makes it his business to find out all about it.

There is no one in all the Green Forest, or on all the Green Meadows, whom Reddy Fox so dislikes to get a glimpse of when he is out hunting as Sammy Jay. If Reddy could count on all the dinners he has failed to get because of Sammy Jay, he would have enough to live on the rest of his life. Anyway, that is what he says. It is a funny thing, but Sammy Jay has the reputation of being a rogue and mischievous, and of being the friend of no one, unless it be his cousin, Blacky the Crow, when the truth is, Sammy is one of the best friends the little people of the Green Forest and the

Green Meadows have. He probably has saved more lives than any other among them. He has saved them by giving warning of danger.

It was very early in the morning, just after jolly, round, red Mr. Sun had begun his climb up in the blue, blue sky, that Sammy Jay started to fly over the Green Meadows, just at the edge of Farmer Brown's corn-field. As he drew near that part of the field where the carrots grew in rows and rows, Sammy's sharp eyes caught sight of something red. Sammy did n't need to look twice to know what it was. He had seen it too often not to recognize it.

"Ha, ha!" exclaimed Sammy. "Ha, ha, and ho, ho! I wonder what mischief Reddy Fox is planning over there? I did n't know that anybody was living there. Reddy seems to be watching something in that old ditch. I believe I'll do a little watching myself."

So Sammy flew to the nearest tree from which he could keep an eye on Reddy Fox. Reddy was so intent on watching that hole of Jerry Muskrat's that he did n't see Sammy. Reddy had left his place during the night long enough to hunt for some Meadow Mice and then returned to watch that hole. He had jumped down in the ditch and with his wonderful nose had made sure that Jerry had not left it. Now he intended to stay right there until Jerry should come out.

If he had known that inquisitive Sammy Jay was watching him, his plans would have been quite suddenly changed.

CHAPTER XXIX

JERRY GETS A WARNING FROM SAMMY JAY

When you hear a warning, heed it.
Never think you do not need it.

Jerry Muskrat.

THERE is one thing which the little people of the Green Forest and the Green Meadows, the Old Pasture, the Old Orchard, the Smiling Pool and the Laughing Brook learned long before human beings, and that is that safety first is the most important thing in a long and happy life. As perhaps you know, most of these little people are constantly in danger. So it has come about that one of the very first things taught their babies is to heed every warning. Those who do not seldom live long.

When Jerry Muskrat had made good his escape from Reddy Fox that moonlight night among Farmer Brown's carrots, he wisely decided that the thing to do was to stay in his snug little storehouse under the ground until such time as Reddy Fox should become tired of watching for him and go away. You see, he knew Reddy well enough to know that he would be very likely to find that entrance to his tunnel in the drainage ditch and that if he did find it, he would watch it the rest of the night. So Jerry simply curled up and slept until morning.

It was at just about the same time that Sammy Jay left the Green Forest that morning, when Jerry awoke and decided in his own mind that by this time it would probably be perfectly safe to resume work getting carrots for his winter supply. So Jerry poked his head out of the little doorway which opened right underneath the green tops of some of the green carrots and was cleverly hidden by them. Once outside, he sat up and looked about. Everything seemed perfectly safe. No enemy was to be seen anywhere. Jerry went to work digging carrots.

Now, knowing nothing about this little doorway of Jerry's, it never entered the head of Reddy

Fox to look over among the carrots. He simply lay on the bank of the ditch, with his eyes fixed on that other entrance to the tunnel, so of course he did n't see Jerry. He could n't have seen Jerry very well, anyway, on account of the tops of the green carrots and the fact that Jerry was some little distance away. Neither did Sammy Jay see Jerry.

For a long time Sammy watched Reddy Fox and Reddy Fox watched the hole to the tunnel in Jerry's ditch. Then Sammy's patience gave out. He flew straight over Reddy, and looking down with his sharp inquisitive eyes, he saw the little hole at the bottom of the ditch. He had n't the remotest idea who could have dug that hole, but just on general principles, Sammy yelled a warning. "Thief! Thief! Thief!" he yelled and flew away about his own business.

At the first sound of Sammy's voice, Jerry Muskrat seized a carrot and darted into his tunnel. He did n't know what the danger was, but he meant to be safe.

CHAPTER XXX

A MYSTERIOUS DISAPPEARANCE

This much to me is very clear
Things of themselves don't disappear.
Jerry Muskrat.

MYSTERIOUS is a long word, but, like many another long word, its meaning is quite simple. A thing which is mysterious is something you do not understand and cannot explain. You just know that it is and that is all. If you go about in the Green Forest a great deal, you will have many mysterious experiences until you have learned to see and hear and to understand what is going on about you.

The instant Reddy Fox heard the voice of Sammy Jay, he knew that there would be no use in keeping watch of that hole at the bottom of the ditch any longer. He knew that Jerry Muskrat probably had heard Sammy's warning. Reddy looked up at Sammy flying over the Green Meadows, and if looks could have hurt, Sammy Jay certainly would have been hurt right then and there. But looks cannot hurt and Sammy went about his business without giving Reddy Fox another thought. As for Reddy, he turned and trotted back to his home in the Old Pasture.

After this, at all hours of the day and night, Reddy Fox might have been seen creeping up to the edge of that old drainage ditch where Jerry Muskrat had made his tunnel. Sometimes it would be early in the morning; sometimes it would be late in the afternoon; sometimes it would be just after the coming of the Black Shadows; sometimes it would be in the moonlight. Always he hoped to surprise Jerry Muskrat and always he failed.

Then Reddy decided to try a new plan. He had discovered that Jerry was still getting carrots, so he decided to hide among the carrots and try to catch Jerry there. It was a moonlight night when he first tried it. Reddy lay flat down among the green tops of the carrots. By and by, seemingly out of nowhere at all, Jerry Muskrat appeared and began to dig up a carrot. He was some little distance away and Reddy began very, very carefully to creep toward Jerry. Suddenly Jerry disappeared. His disappearance was just as mysterious as his appearance had been.

Reddy raised himself on his hind legs to look over the tops of the carrots, to see if any were moving in a way to show where Jerry was.

Not a leaf moved. It must be that Jerry was lying flat down on the ground.

Reddy ran lightly down between the rows where he had last seen Jerry, but there was no Jerry there. He tried the next row with the same result. Then he began to get excited, and raced up and down all the rows, but no Jerry. This was too much for Reddy. He was positive that Jerry could not have reached the drainage ditch without being seen, yet Jerry had disappeared. Reddy finally gave up and went home to think it over. Such a disappearance certainly was mysterious.

CHAPTER XXXI

THE SECRET IS OUT

The thing you 've puzzled most about
Is simple once you 've found it out.
Jerry Muskrat.

REDDY FOX does not like mysteries. One reason is that he is so clever and smart that he cannot bear to think that there is anything he cannot find out. The mysterious disappearance of Jerry Muskrat over in Farmer Brown's carrot patch troubled Reddy a great deal. The truth is, he could n't think of anything else. He had an uncomfortable feeling that somehow Jerry Muskrat had fooled him, and this hurt his pride.

Of course, Reddy could n't keep away from that carrot patch very long. In fact, he was back there again that very same night; but this time he did n't see anything of Jerry. Very early the next morning he made another visit to the carrot patch. This time he hid right close to the place where he had seen Jerry. He had been there only a few minutes when he turned his head for something; and when he looked back, there sat Jerry right in front of him. Reddy gasped. He had n't heard a sound, yet there sat Jerry as big as life. He was n't more than two jumps away. Reddy crouched to make those two springs. Just as he did so, a Merry Little Breeze passed and carried the scent of Reddy straight over to Jerry.

Reddy made the first of the two necessary jumps and, like a flash, Jerry disappeared. Reddy's second jump landed him on nothing at all but the ground.

"Ha!" exclaimed Reddy. He was no longer fooled. He knew now what had become of Jerry. No one could disappear like that except into the ground. "Why did n't I think of that before?" muttered Reddy. "That fellow's got a hole around here somewhere, as sure as I have a white tip to my tail." Two minutes later his nose led him to Jerry's hole under the spreading tops of the carrots.

Reddy was sorely tempted to try to dig Jerry out, but he remembered the hole in the ditch and he guessed right away that Jerry had a long tunnel, of which these two holes were the entrances. It would be of no use to dig for Jerry, because all he would have to do would be to run through his tunnel and out of the other entrance into the ditch.

Reddy thought for about two minutes and then he headed for the Old Pasture as fast as he could run. He had a plan which he felt sure would succeed this time.

CHAPTER XXXII

WHY REDDY'S PLAN FAILED

That which is too much for one
May, perhaps, by two be done.

Jerry Muskrat.

REDDY FOX did n't waste any time. He knew exactly what Jerry Muskrat had done. It was very clear to him now why he had failed to find any trace of Jerry Muskrat in the drainage ditch between Jerry's hole and the Laughing Brook. Of course Jerry had n't been going back to the Laughing Brook and the Smiling Pool at all. He had been living up there in that new tunnel of his, while he laid in a supply of carrots for the winter.

When Reddy reached home in the Old Pasture, he found that Mrs. Reddy was not there. This was a great disappointment. You see, Reddy needed Mrs. Reddy's help. He pointed his nose straight up at the sky and barked. He waited a little, then barked again. After a while he barked a third time. This time he got an answer. He knew that Mrs. Reddy was coming, so he sat down to wait as patiently as he could.

Presently Mrs. Reddy arrived and Reddy told her all about Jerry Muskrat and the tunnel from the drainage ditch to the carrot patch.

"We'll go down there at once,

my dear," said Reddy. "You will watch at one entrance, and I will watch at the other. We will have to have a lot of patience, but sooner or later we will have a Muskrat dinner as a reward."

So Reddy and Mrs. Reddy hurried back across the Green Meadows to the drainage ditch and the carrot patch. It was such a simple plan that it seemed certain to succeed. Mrs. Reddy hid where she could watch the doorway in the little ditch. Reddy went straight to the doorway which opened among the carrots. There another thought came to Reddy. It would be easy digging up there in the carrot patch so why not save time by digging and so frighten Jerry that he would run out and try to make his escape to his home in the Smiling Pool?

So Reddy dug and Mrs. Reddy watched. But Jerry Muskrat did n't appear. Finally Reddy gave up digging. He had begun to suspect that he was tiring himself out for nothing. He was, too. You see, Jerry Muskrat had guessed right away what would happen when Reddy discovered that entrance among the carrots.

"He knows where both entrances are now," thought Jerry, "and he 'll go right off and get Mrs. Reddy or Old Granny Fox to watch at one, while he watches at the other. I 've got carrots enough stored away to last me all winter, so I'll just get back to the Smiling Pool while there is a chance."

So while Reddy was getting Mrs. Reddy to help him, Jerry slipped out into the drainage ditch and scampered as fast as his legs could take him, back to the Laughing Brook, and then swam down to the Smiling Pool. There he climbed out on the Big Rock, from which he could look out across the Green Meadows. Presently he began to chuckle. He could see Reddy and Mrs. Reddy hurrying across the Green Meadows towards the carrot patch.

CHAPTER XXXIII

REDDY FOX GIVES UP

Waste no time on foolish wishes;
They are much like uncaught fishes.

Jerry Muskrat.

IT was hard work for Reddy Fox to admit that Jerry Muskrat had been too smart for him. You know it comes hard to all clever people to admit that others are as smart or smarter than they. But when Reddy Fox had dug until he was tired, and still had not frightened Jerry Muskrat out of his tunnel, which ran from Farmer Brown's carrot patch to the drainage ditch where Mrs. Reddy was watching, he felt very certain that Jerry was no longer there. So he stopped digging and went over to join Mrs. Reddy.

"Well," she snapped, "where is that Muskrat dinner you promised me?"

Even then, Reddy wanted to find some excuse. Maybe you know just how Reddy felt.

"He probably slipped out of here while you had your head turned," said Reddy, trying to put the blame on Mrs. Reddy. Mrs. Reddy's eyes snapped.

"Why don't you tell the truth?" she said sharply. "You know well enough that Jerry Muskrat was out of here long before we got here. You brought me over here for nothing, and you know it." With this Mrs. Reddy turned her back and trotted off towards the Old Pasture.

Reddy could n't find a word to say. With the most sheepish look on his face you could imagine, he watched Mrs. Reddy disappear. When she was out of sight, he jumped down in the ditch and sniffed eagerly along the bottom. Jerry had been along there. There was n't the least doubt about that. Reddy leaped out on the bank and started straight for the Smiling Pool. Very cautiously he crawled up and peeped over the bank. There on the Big Rock sat Jerry Muskrat. Jerry looked very well pleased with something, and it was n't difficult for Reddy to guess what.

Reddy drew back his lips in a way to show all his teeth and in his eyes was an ugly look; but he did n't show himself. He would n't give Jerry Muskrat the pleasure of seeing how angry and upset he was. He stole away and hurried over to a certain quiet place in the Green Forest, where he could be alone and sulk until he recovered his temper.

"That fellow is n't worth trying to catch, anyway," he muttered, as he trotted along. "I never did care much for Muskrat and I don't know what I should have done with him if I had caught him."

Would n't Jerry Muskrat have laughed if he could have heard that?

CHAPTER XXXIV

JERRY'S FEARS ARE ENDED

Nothing ever simply happens;
Bear this point in mind.
If you look but close enough,
A cause you 'll surely find.

Jerry Muskrat.

FOR a week Jerry Muskrat had been finding good things at several of his favorite eating places—things of which he was very fond. They had been put there by a stranger who visited the Laughing Brook and the Smiling Pool every day. At first, Jerry had been very suspicious. He had feared a trap at each of those places where the good things were. But he had found no trace of a trap and by the end of the week he had ceased to think of traps at all.

The result was that now Jerry thought of nothing but the good things to eat, and scrambled up on the bank and the old log which lay partly in the water, as carelessly as he had been in the habit of doing before the stranger appeared. His one thought was to get those good things the stranger so thoughtfully left there for him. No longer was he troubled by any uncomfortable suspicions.

"I don't believe that this is the trapper of whom Billy Mink and Bobby Coon have warned me," thought Jerry. "It must have been some one else who set those traps that Billy Mink says he found. This is a friend. I don't know why he takes so much interest in me and brings me all these good things, and I don't care. I hope he 'll keep right on bringing me apples, carrots and such things. They certainly do taste good to me. Yes, siree, they certainly do taste good to me."

Sometimes the stranger came early in the morning and sometimes he came late in the afternoon. Always he left something for Jerry, and Jerry was very grateful. These feasts saved him a lot of time and trouble hunting for food. It gave him more time to work on his house and make it ready for winter. Jerry had a feeling that the winter was going to be a hard one and he intended to be fully prepared for it. So he worked hard, making the roof and walls of his house thicker than usual, and digging tunnels in the banks of the Smiling Pool so that no matter how hard the winter might be, he would be quite comfortable.

Jerry so lost all fear of that stranger that sometimes he would work when he knew that the stranger was watching him. However, he always took care to see that the stranger had no gun with him. Had the stranger carried a gun, Jerry would have kept out of sight and would at once have been suspicious. As it was, he would keep right on working until the stranger left; then hurry over to see what the stranger had left for him. Jerry was very happy and quite without fear.

CHAPTER XXXV

JERRY HAS A SAD AWAKENING

The trouble is that troubles are
More frequently than not
Brought on by naught but carelessness
By some one who forgot.

Jerry Muskrat.

ONE day the stranger visited the Smiling Pool, as he had been doing for more than a week. Jerry Muskrat kept right on working on his house. All the time he kept a bright eye on the stranger, to see what he was doing. As usual, the stranger visited each of Jerry's favorite eating places. It seemed to Jerry that he stayed at each spot a little longer than usual, but

THERE HE SAT DOWN AND BEGAN TO EAT.

Jerry did n't think anything of that.

Just as soon as the stranger left, Jerry swam straight over to a certain old log, which lay half in the water and half on the bank. He felt sure that on the upper part of that old log he would find some pieces of apple or carrot. He was n't disappointed. Even before he could see them his nose told him they were there. Now ordinarily Jerry climbed right up that old log out of the water, but this time he did n't. It just happened so, that was all. He climbed out on the bank beside the log and then up on the log. There he sat down and began to eat. My, how good those pieces of apple and carrot did taste! You see, Jerry had been working very hard and he had a splendid appetite.

At first he sat facing the water. After a while he changed his position so that he was back to the water and his tail dropped down in the water where it covered the lower part of that old log. Snap! With a squeal of pain and fright, Jerry jumped right up in the air. He lost his balance and fell off the old log. Then he tried to scramble away. He could n't. Something was holding him by his tail and pinching it most dreadfully. Jerry was too frightened to think. He could n't imagine what dreadful thing had got him. He pulled and pulled until it seemed to him that he must pull his tail out by the roots. Finally, he twisted around to see what held him. It was a trap! The stout, cruel jaws of it were gripping his tail about an inch from the end.

Then Jerry understood. He awakened to the truth, and it was a sad awakening. That stranger was a trapper, after all! He had been putting those good things there for Jerry, so that Jerry would get so used to finding them that his suspicions would be put to sleep. When he was quite sure that Jerry had grown careless, and was no longer suspicious of traps, he had placed a trap on that old log just under water. If Jerry had climbed up on that old log as usual, he would have stepped in that trap and been caught by a leg. As it was, he had accidentally sprung it with his tail.

Being caught by the tail was bad enough, but it would have been worse to have been caught by a leg, though Jerry did n't stop to think of this at the time. So far as he could see, it did n't make any difference how he was caught. Poor Jerry! He was so frightened that for the time being he hardly noticed the pain.

CHAPTER XXXVI

JERRY MUSKRAT NURSES A SORE TAIL

"Look before you leap," we 're told
A saying wise and tried and old.
Think before you jump, I say,
You may not jump at all that way.
Jerry Muskrat.

JERRY MUSKRAT was caught in a cruel, steel trap. He was caught by his tail. It was a fortunate thing for him that it was by his tail and not by a leg. But right at the time, Jerry could n't see anything fortunate in it. In fact, to Jerry's way of thinking, it was wholly unfortunate.

Now, Jerry Muskrat is much more at home in the water than

on land, and his first impulse in time of danger is to get into the water at once, if he is not already there. So when that cruel, steel trap caught him by the tail in its wicked jaws, Jerry plunged back off the old log into the water and tried to swim away. If he had only known it, this was just what the trapper had expected him to do and had hoped he would do. That trap had been fastened with a chain in such a way that Jerry could get into deep water. You see, the trapper hoped that Jerry would drown himself, and Jerry did come pretty near doing just that thing. He swam with all his might, but the trap held him; and as he struggled, he lost his breath and water got up his nose in such a way that he choked.

It did n't take him very long to realize that he could n't pull himself free in the water. At first, he was in such a panic of fright that he did n't use his wits at all. But after he began to realize that by struggling in the water he would simply drown himself, Jerry's wits began to work. He turned about and swam back to that old log and climbed out on it. There he squatted down and rested to regain his strength and get his breath.

"It 's of no use for me to try to pull myself free by swimming," thought Jerry. "I 'm a pretty strong swimmer, but not strong enough to do that. Perhaps I can pull myself free up here."

So when he had rested, Jerry dug his claws into the old log and pulled and pulled and pulled. It seemed to him that he certainly was pulling his tail out by the roots. But it would be better to do that and have no tail at all, than to lose his life. So he pulled and pulled and pulled. By and by, it seemed to him that he felt his tail slipping a little. That gave him courage and he pulled harder than ever.

Suddenly he pitched right over on his head and at the same time there was a little snap behind him. He had pulled his tail free and the jaws of the trap had come together. You see, Jerry's tail tapers, and he had been caught not very far from the end of it. It was this which saved him.

As soon as he felt himself free, Jerry plunged into the water and swam over to his house. Not until he was safely inside his bedroom did he look at his tail. The skin had been torn by the jaws of the trap and the end of his tail was raw and bleeding. It was dreadfully sore and ached. Jerry began to lick it very gently. For the rest of that day and the following night Jerry stayed right in his house and nursed that sore tail.

CHAPTER XXXVII

JERRY IS FILLED WITH DISTRUST

Lest your judgment you would mend,
Hold it 'til you see the end.

Jerry Muskrat.

As Jerry Muskrat lay in his bed, safe in his house, nursing his sore tail, he had time to do a lot of thinking and he did do a lot of thinking. He thought of how day after day he had found all those good things to eat at each of his favorite eating places and how there had not been one single thing to make him suspicious. In fact, there had been everything to take suspicion away. He began to understand just what that trapper had tried to do and it seemed to him that nothing could possibly have been more unfair.

"He tried to make me think he was my friend," thought Jerry. "He knew that if I had the least suspicion that he was n't my friend, I would be watching for traps. So he pretended that he was my friend and he brought all those nice things for me to eat so that I would trust him. I did trust him and he knew it. Then, when he was sure that I would n't suspect him of doing such a thing, he set that awful trap for me. I'll never trust anybody again. I never, never will. It's awful to distrust everybody, but after this I'll just have to."

So Jerry Muskrat was filled with distrust. He had been so very happy there in the Smiling Pool for so long, that now life seemed hardly worth while. There was no happiness in it. You see, he felt that not only could he no longer trust those who seemed to be his friends, but he was suspicious of everything. He no longer dared to climb out on his favorite places along the bank. He was even suspicious of the Big Rock. The only place where he felt absolutely safe was right inside his own house.

But, of course, he could n't stay in his own house all the time. He had to eat. Of course. Everybody has to eat. Then, too, he had some work yet to do on that house of his to make it ready for the winter. This meant that he had to travel around considerably to get his food and to get the material for his house. But now he never went ashore without first looking with the greatest care for signs of a trap.

One of the first things he did, after he got through nursing his sore tail, was to go to each of the places where that trapper had put good things to eat. He went there, not to get those good things, but to find out if there were traps there, as there had been on the old log. He found a trap at each place. After that, he did not go near those places. Billy Mink would have found a way to get all those good things to eat without getting into one of the traps, but Jerry preferred to take no chances. He simply kept away from those places. Those pieces of carrot and apple were a terrible temptation, but he contented himself with his regular food and tried to forget that there were such things as carrots and apples. And even when he was hunting for his regular food, he was all the time watching out for traps. He was so filled with distrust that he took no joy in anything.

CHAPTER XXXVIII

FARMER BROWN'S BOY LOSES HIS TEMPER

Alas, that man so seldom pauses
To think of all the pain he causes.

Jerry Muskrat.

IT was a long time since Farmer Brown's Boy had visited the Laughing Brook and the Smiling Pool, so of course he knew nothing about what had been going on there. One morning, having nothing else to do, he took it into his head to go over to the Smiling Pool to see how Jerry Muskrat was getting along. Jerry saw him coming and his heart was so filled with distrust because of what he had suffered from the trapper, who had so nearly caught him, that he actually suspected Farmer Brown's Boy.

"I used to think that I could trust Farmer Brown's Boy," muttered Jerry, "but I don't trust him. I don't trust anybody. As likely as not, Farmer Brown's Boy has been friendly just so that he can take advantage of it." So Jerry promptly hid where Farmer Brown's Boy could not see him, but where he could watch Farmer Brown's Boy.

The latter was whistling, a habit he has when he is feeling happy. He came straight down to the bank of the Smiling Pool, and there he stood for a few minutes, looking at Jerry's house.

"I guess you are pretty nearly ready for cold weather," said he, just as if he were talking to Jerry. "I've brought a couple of carrots for you and I hope you'll enjoy them. You'll find them over by that favorite old log of yours."

Farmer Brown's Boy pulled a couple of carrots from his pocket and walked over to the old log, which lay half in the water and half out. It was the very log where Jerry had been caught in the trap by his tail. When Farmer Brown's Boy got there, he gave a little whistle of surprise. There were some pieces of carrot already there. Then Farmer Brown's Boy's face clouded.

"I wonder what this means," said he, and at once began to look about. It did n't take him long to discover the trap fastened to the old log. "Ha! I thought so!" exclaimed Farmer Brown's Boy, and his face became angry-looking.

He reached down and got hold of the chain of the trap and pulled it free from the log. Then he tossed it up on the bank and at once went over to another favorite feeding place of Jerry's. There, just as he expected, he found another trap. This he also threw up on the bank and his face looked angrier than ever.

Now, Farmer Brown's Boy knew

all about trapping; and, what is more, he knew all about the ways of Jerry Muskrat. So he went from place to place where he thought traps might be set. He found two more, and by this time he had quite lost his temper.

"I'd like to know who it is has dared to set traps here," he grumbled. "This is on our land, and everybody knows that we don't allow trapping. I guess I'll have to go up the Laughing Brook and see if there are more traps up there. I'll take these traps along with me, and whoever owns them will have to come up to the house to get them. Then I'll give him such a piece of my mind that he won't do any more trapping along the Laughing Brook and around the Smiling Pool."

So it was that Farmer Brown's Boy restored peace and happiness to the Smiling Pool and the Laughing Brook, and Jerry Muskrat found that after all there was one whom he could trust.

Longlegs the Heron insists that there shall be a book about him, so that will be the title of the next volume in this series.

THE END